Sally Kindberg's

DRAW IT!

MONSTERS

and other scary stuff

BLOOMSBURY
Activity Books

SQUEAK!
Draw 6 more bats in this cave.

Draw what's in this monster's tummy.

Draw a super-powered broomstick.

Draw the creatures that make these sounds.

Draw something horrid in this sewer.

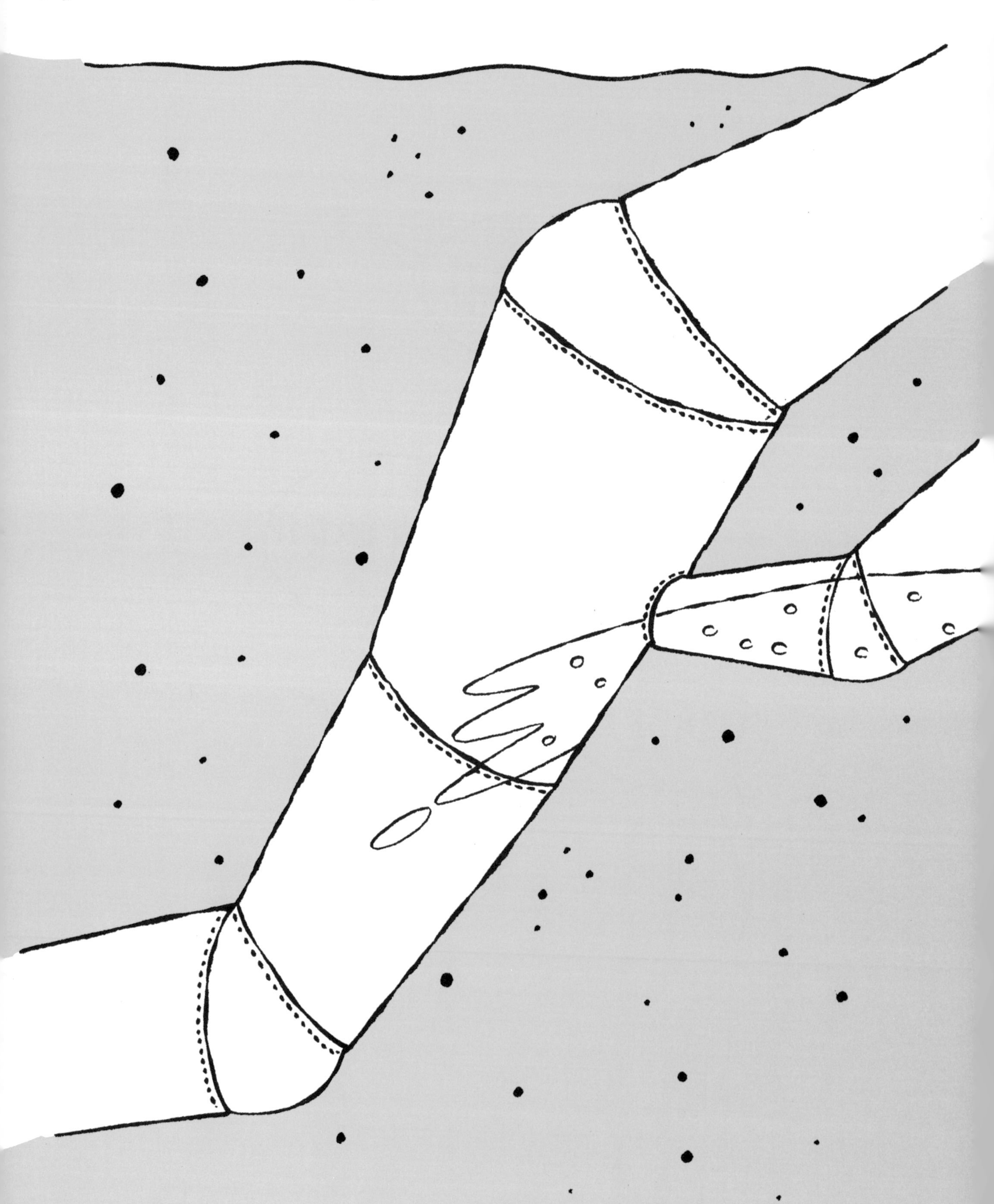

Draw some guests at the annual underwater monster party.

Draw the body for this creature.

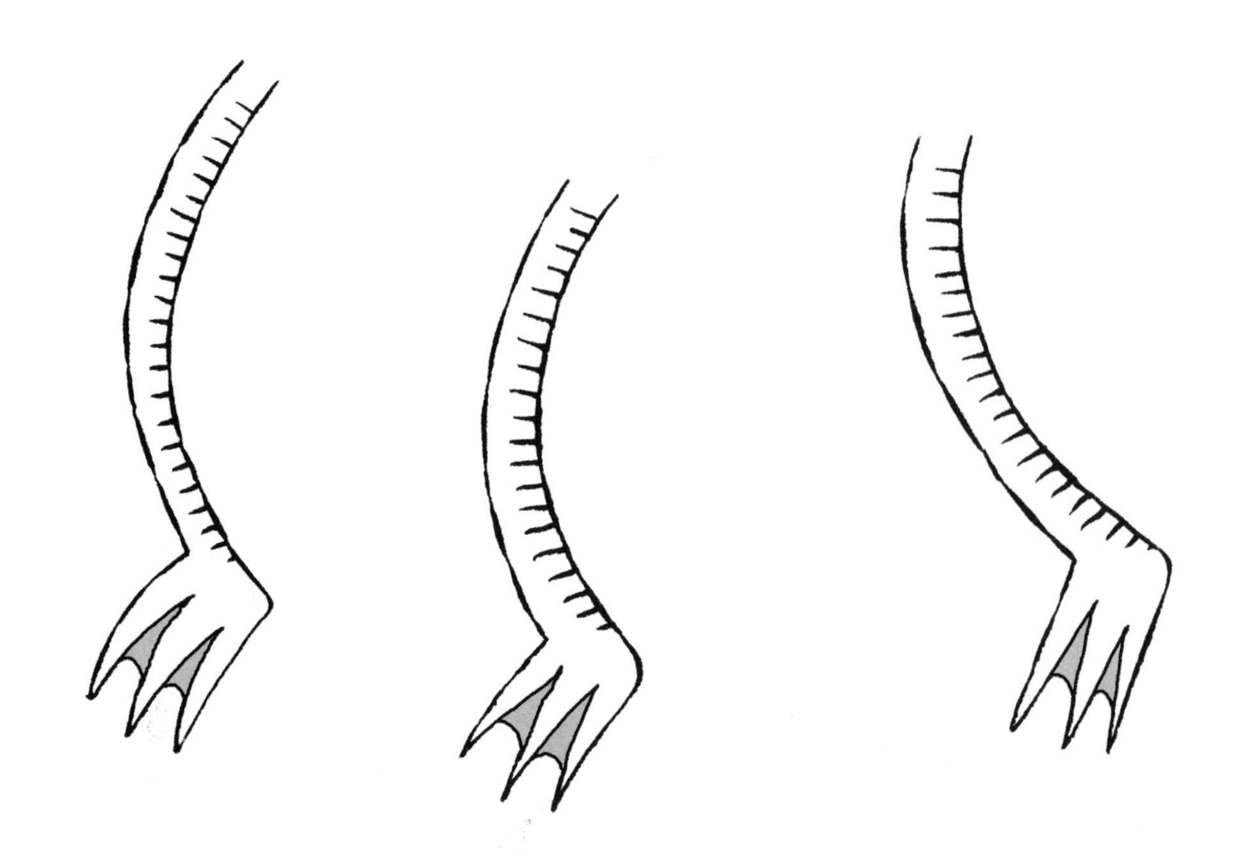

Draw some ghosts at the seaside.

Yum, yum . . .
maggotty
biscuits!
Draw some.

Oh dear,
you've been
abducted by
aliens. How did
that happen?
Draw it!

Draw what's in these jars in Pharaoh's tomb.

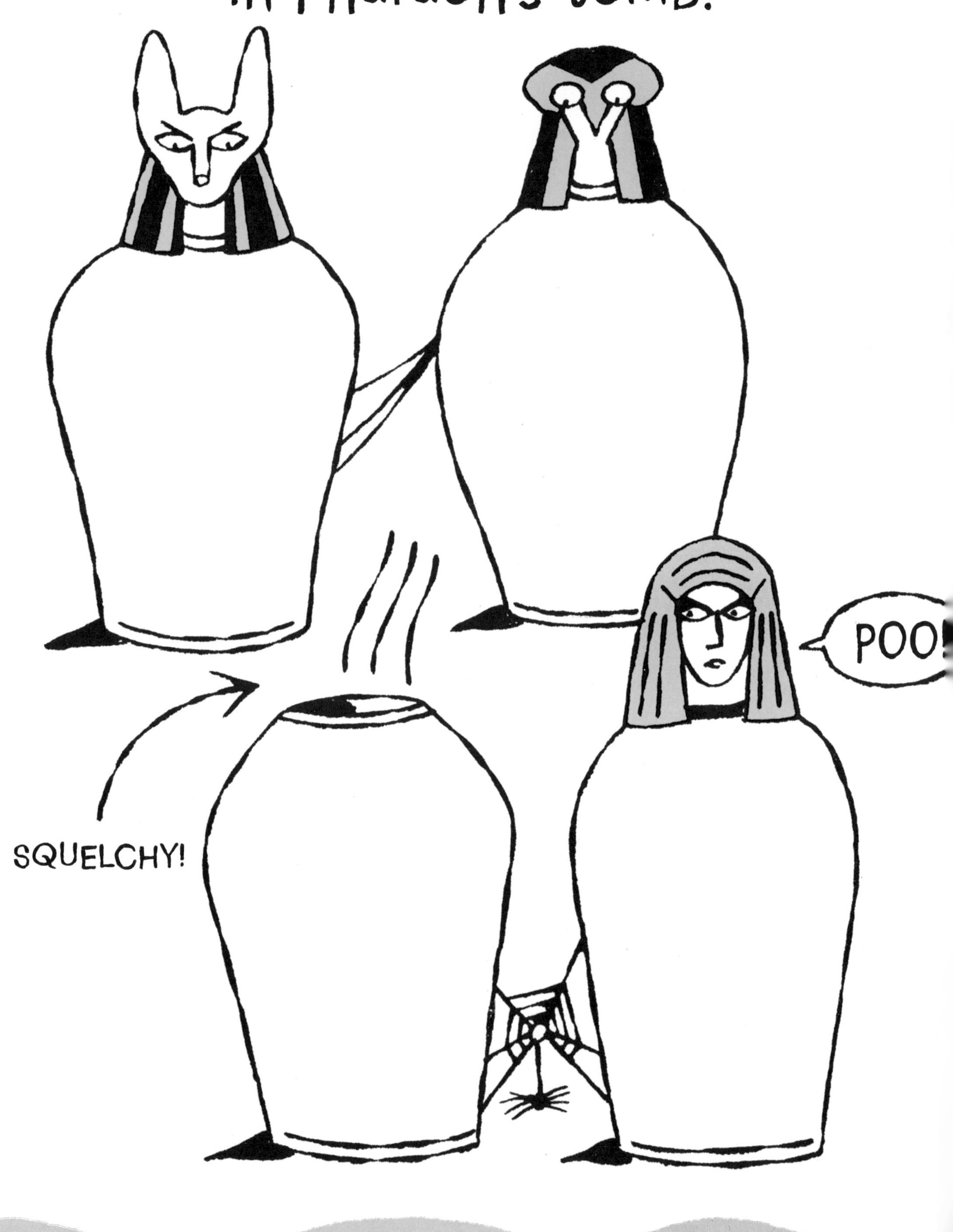

Draw a dragon family having a picnic.

Draw a
ghoul
in love.

Draw some mummies waking up.

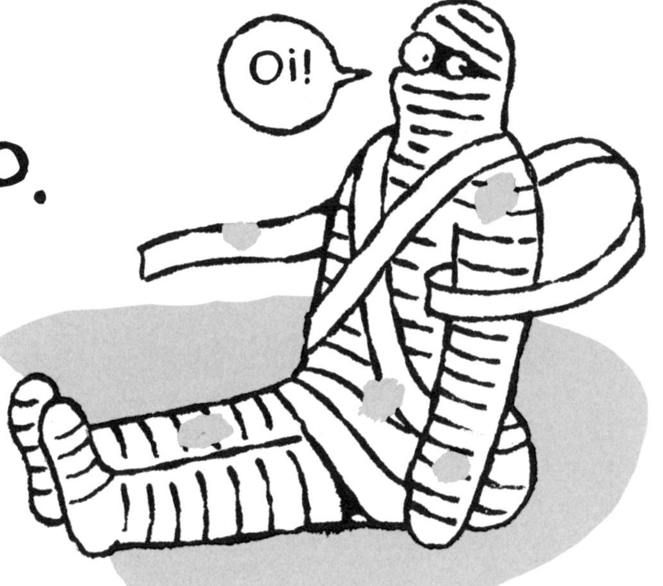

Draw someone
turning into
a werewolf.

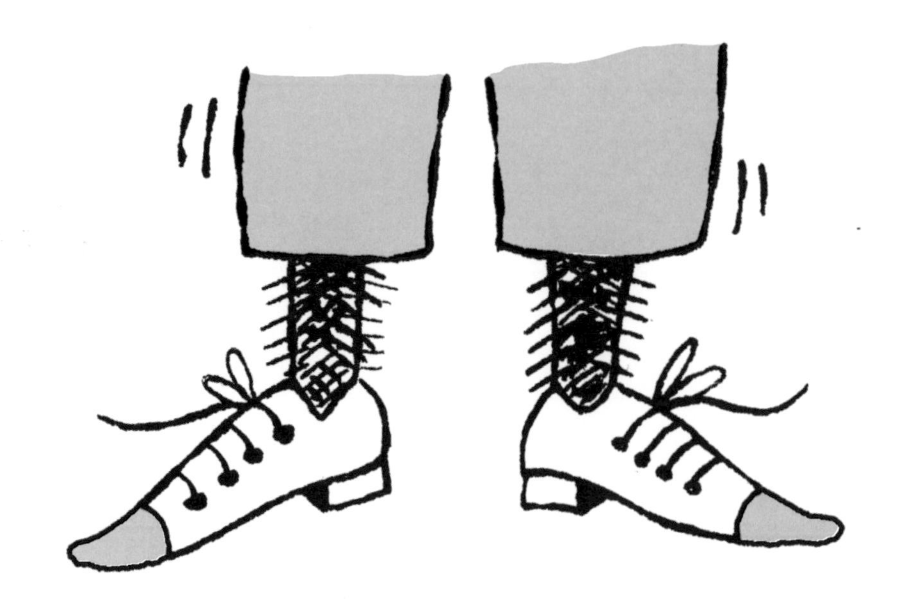

Draw some specs for these spectres.

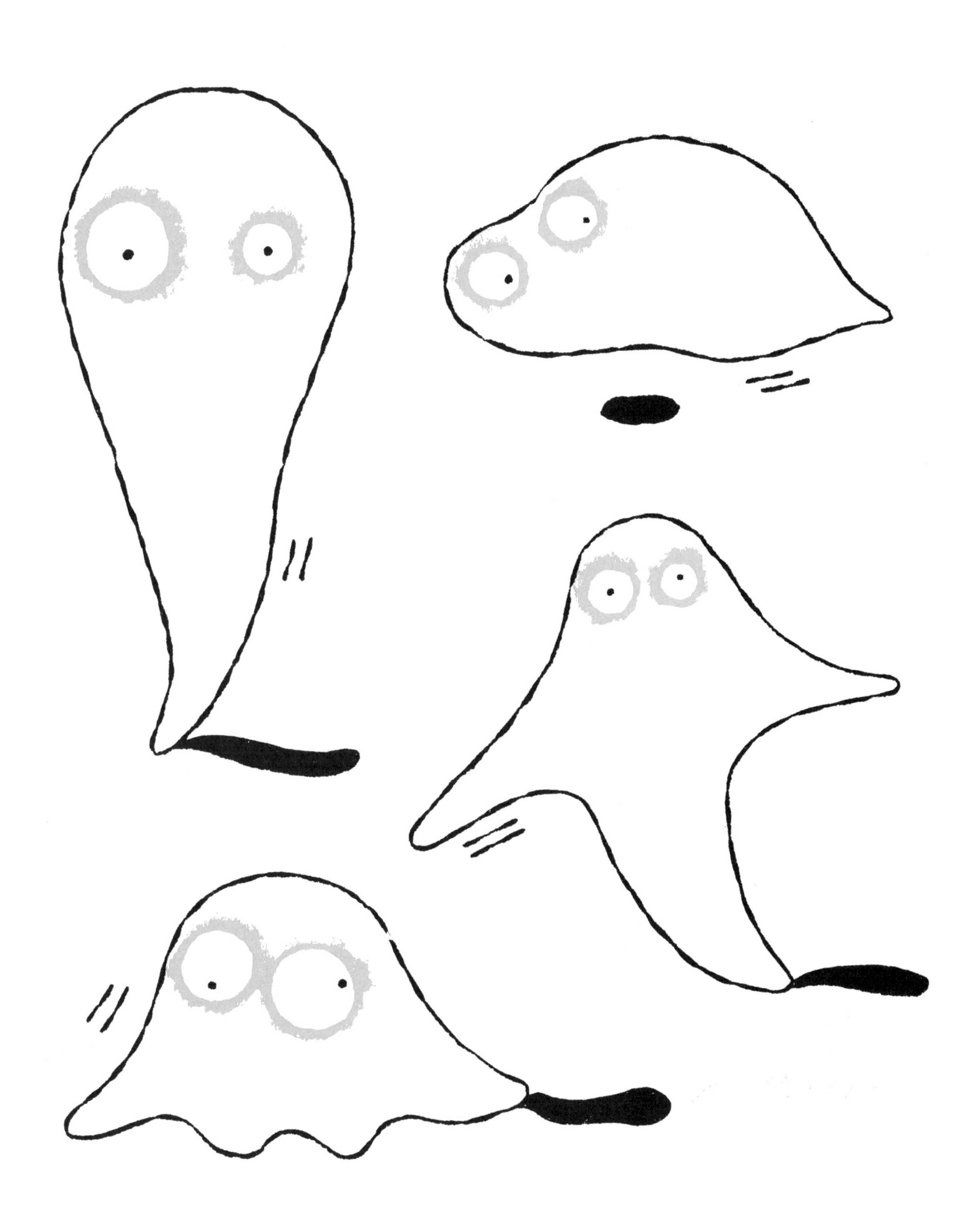

Draw a pet for Dr Frankenstein.

Draw some hairy scuttlers.

Home Smelling fresh and clean? Yuk! Draw some items to leave around for a lovely, sickening stench.

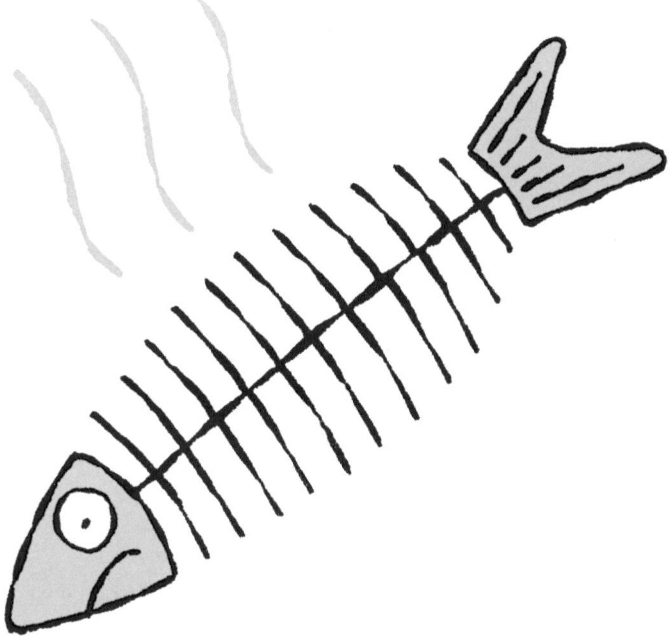

Draw a monster with a streaming cold.

Draw some false teeth for a vampire.

Draw a monster's laundry hung out to get mouldy.

Draw ten different creepy-crawlies.

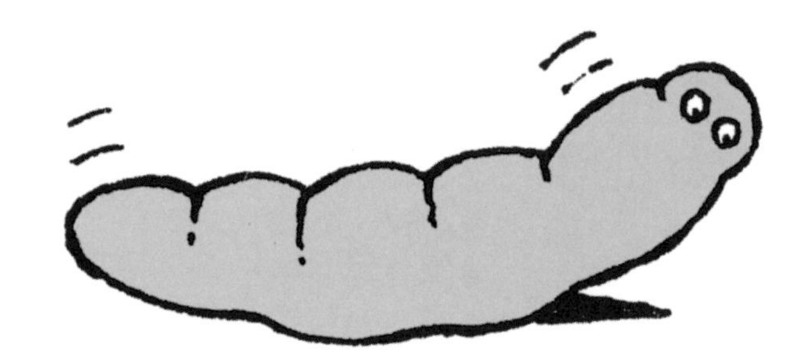

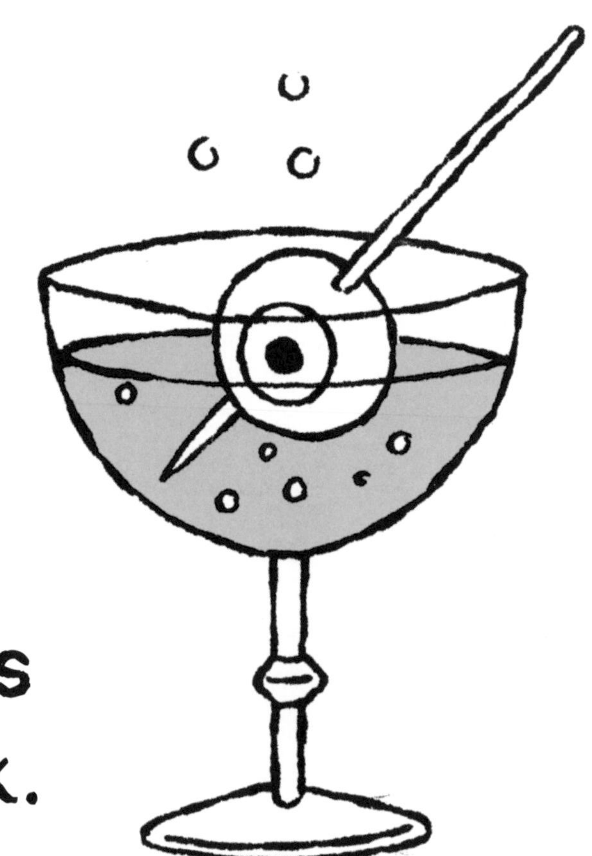

Draw a zombie's
favourite snack.

Draw a flying lesson.

Draw some monsters at their exercise class.

Whee!

Draw a yeti with killer breath.

Draw a monster's nightmare.

Draw some trolls doing cartwheels.

Mmm... old sock scented room spray. Draw a label for it.

Bah!

Draw a goblin in a bad mood.

Draw a
baby ogre
out for a
trample
with his
mother.

Draw a giant spider taking her babies for a stroll.

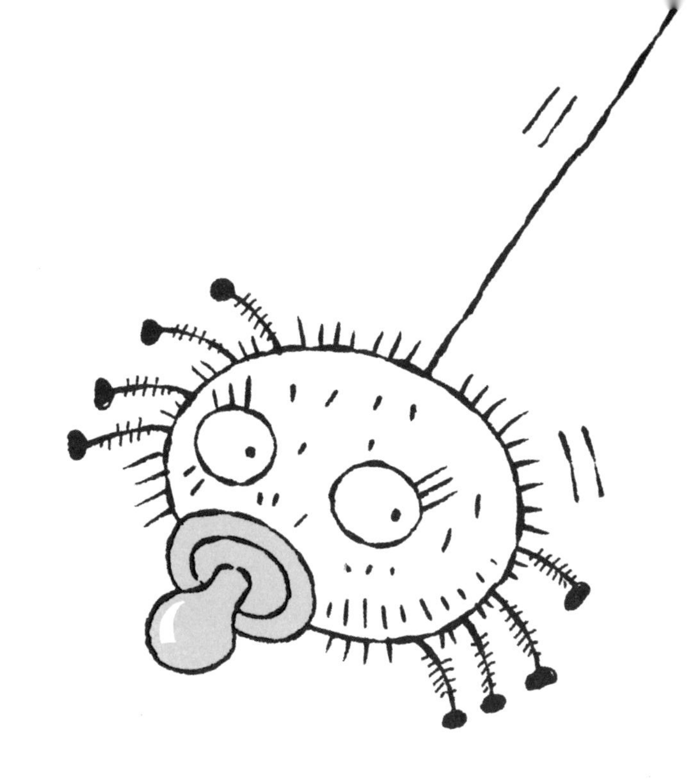

Draw something almost invisible.

Argh! What was THAT?

Draw
a bone
cruncher.

Draw a puddleful of evil-tempered toads.

Draw a get unwell card.

Draw some monsters having a lurking lesson.

Whoops – these eyeballs have come loose. Draw their owners.

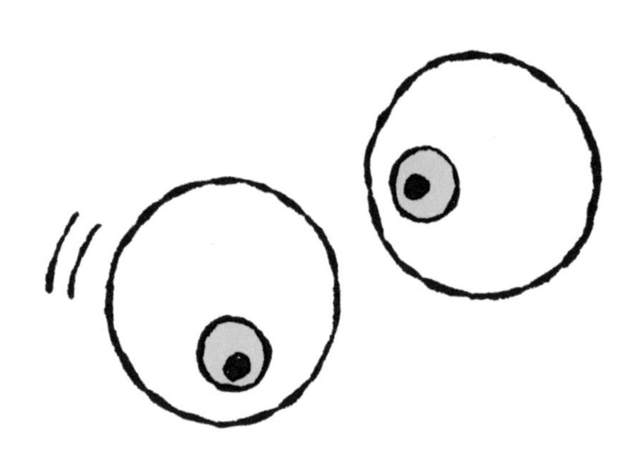

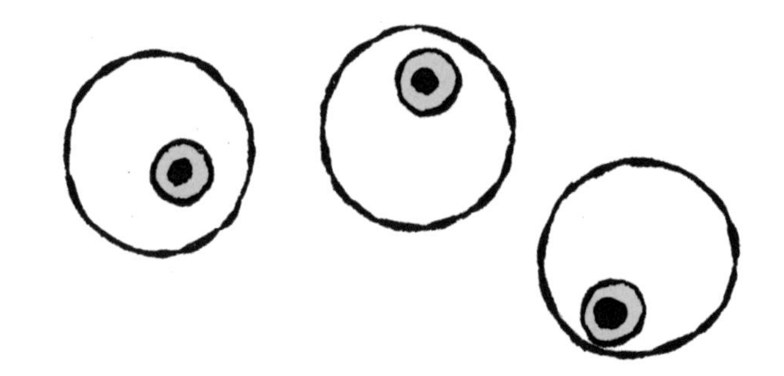

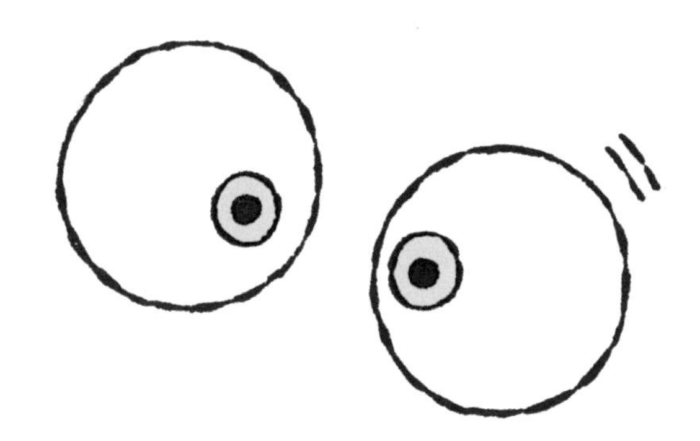

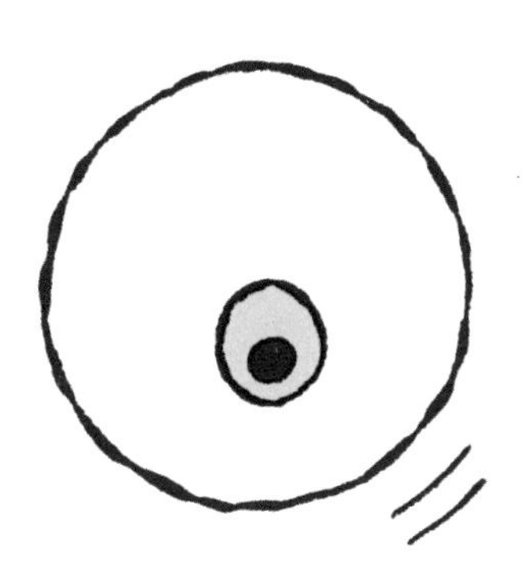

Draw a monster's ghastly grin.

Draw a
shy ghost.

Draw some hairstyles for these characters.

Draw
a ghoul
on a
bike.

Draw some gossiping ghosts.

Draw some skeletons in this cupboard. How many can you fit inside?

Draw
something
that comes
out at
night.

Draw these monsters' family tree.

Draw a witch having a makeover.

Adds wrinkly bits in seconds!

Draw a map of Swampland™.

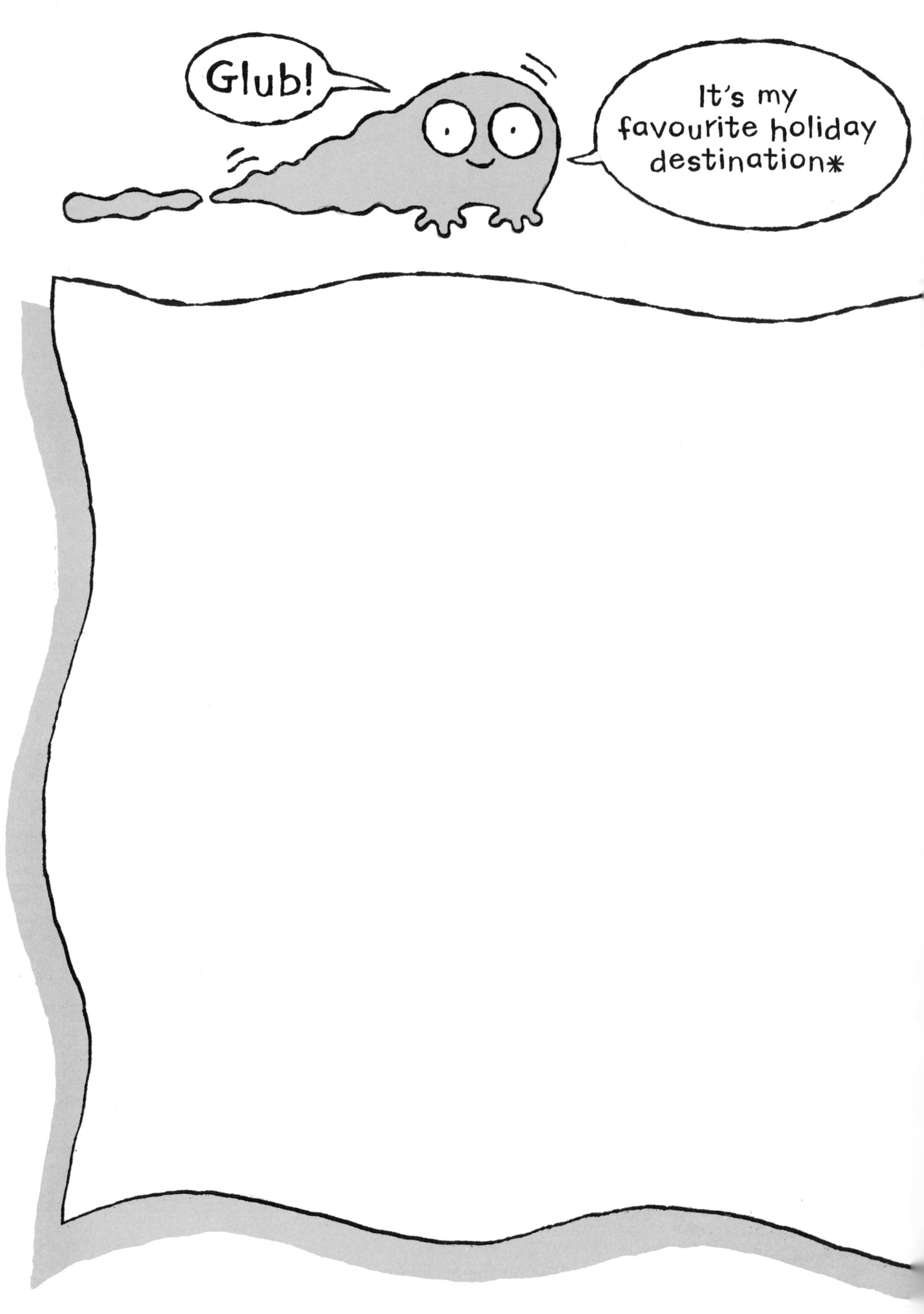

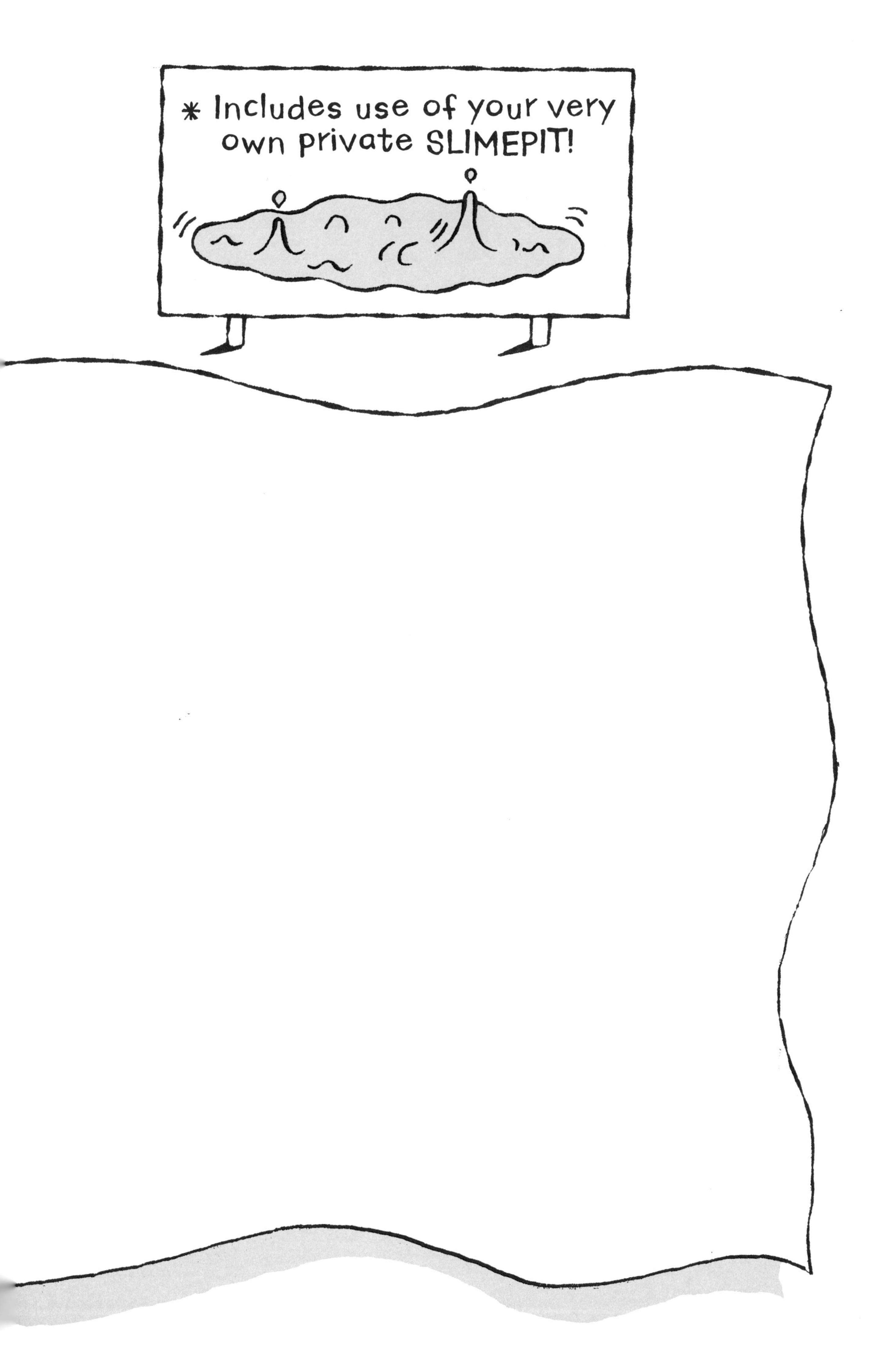
* Includes use of your very own private SLIMEPIT!

Draw a shape-shifter turning into something else.

Draw a witch on a shopping spree.

Draw the Zombies' Sports Day.

Draw some ghastly styles for this claw boutique.

Draw a sea monster's favourite weather.

Draw a haunted suit of armour.

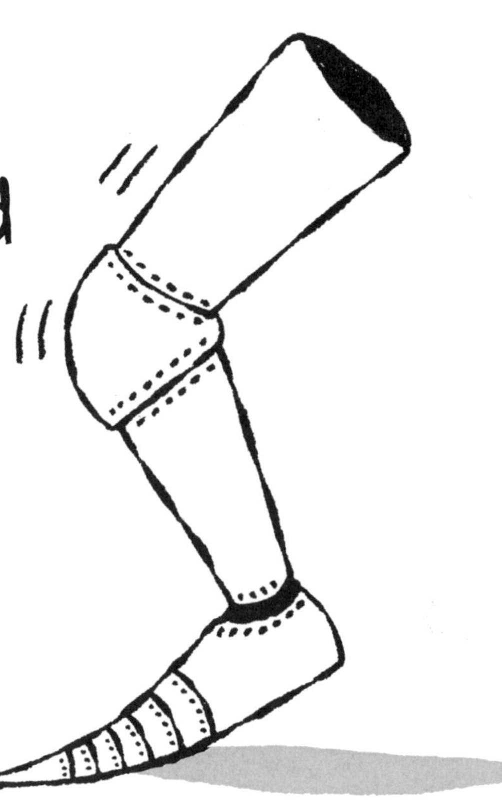

Draw a ghastly menu. Today's specials: Vomit Mousse and Pus Sausage.

Draw some boots designed to keep the damp in.

Draw a
cyclops with
toothache.

Draw your escape from Aliens.

Draw something slithery that lives under this stone.

Draw something unpleasant caught in this cobweb.

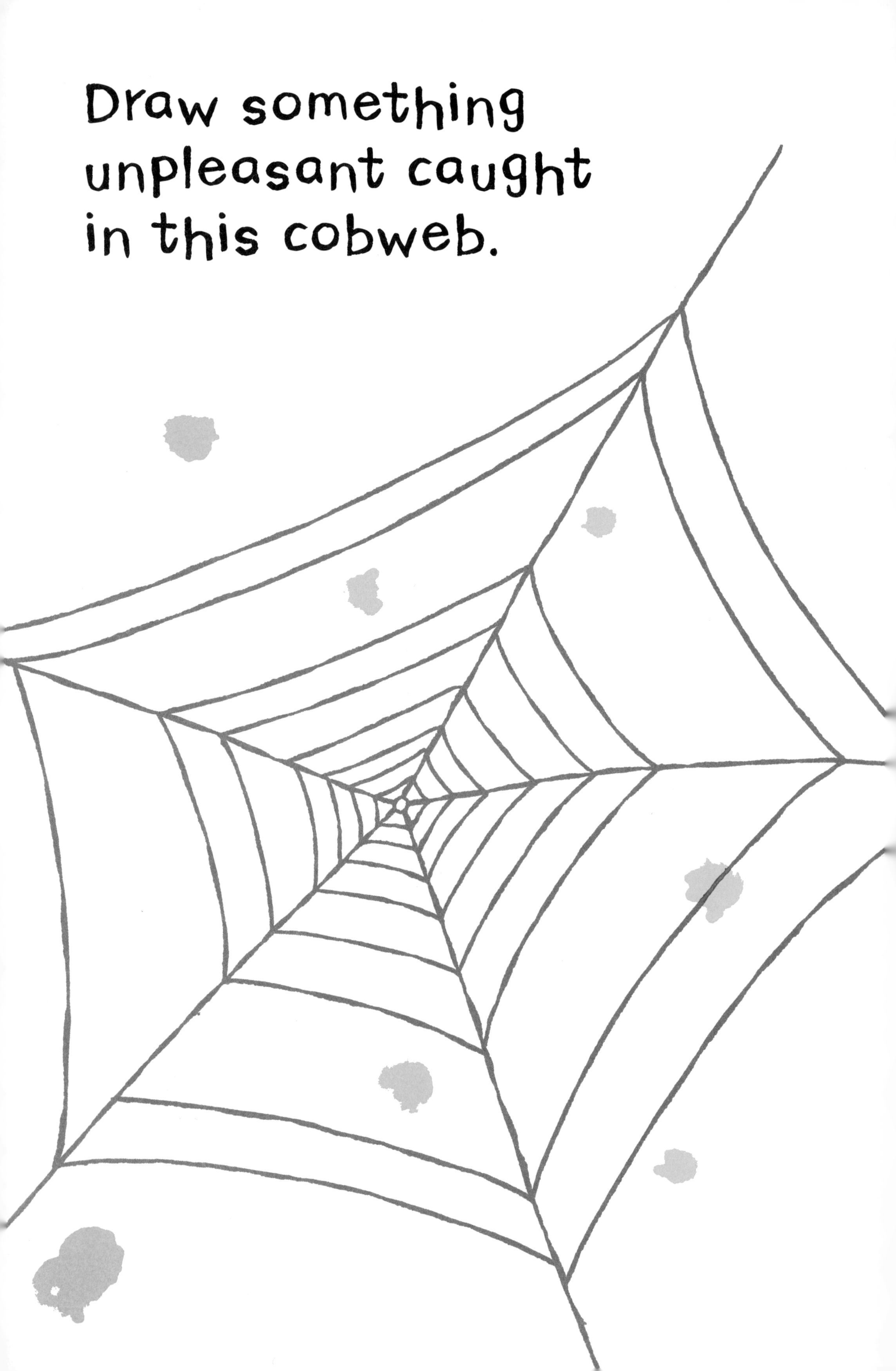

Draw some snakes in this pit.

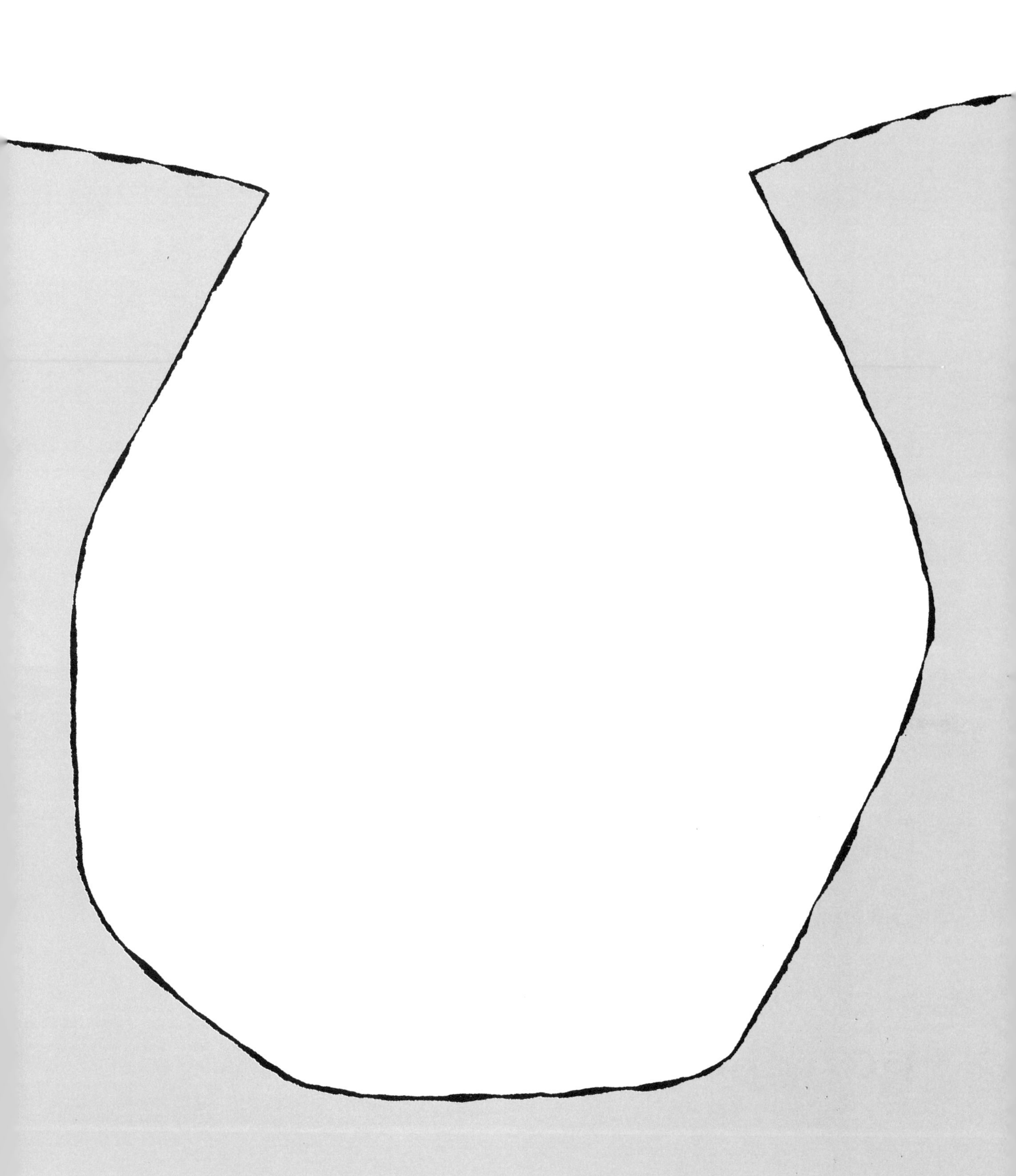

Draw what's in a witch's handbag.

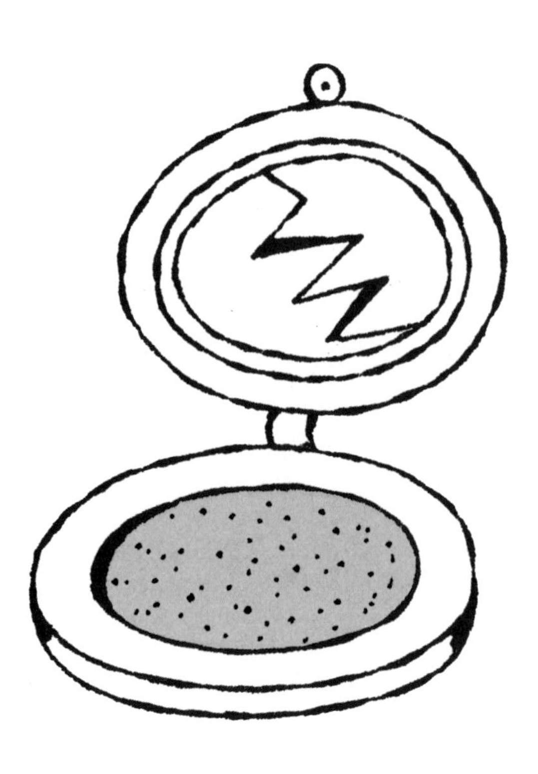

Draw some Gungepaste.

Draw 3 finalists for this year's Ugly Contest.

I'm so proud of my mum!
Runner Up

Draw something vile skulking in this dungeon.

Draw a shrivelled hand (useful for spells).

Draw 4 aliens on a shopping trip to Earth.

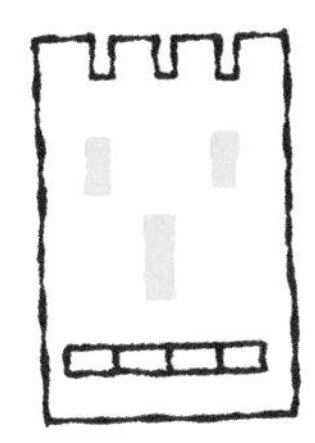

Draw a map of how to get to Creepy Castle.

You could use these symbols or make up your own.

Demon Lair

Get Lost Woods

Sinking Sands

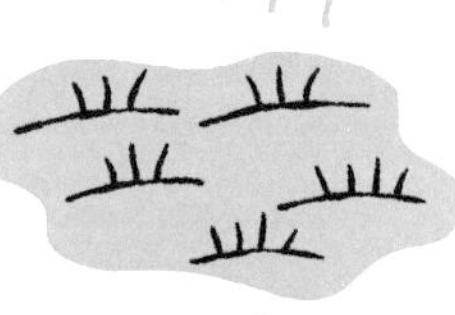

Murky Marsh

Draw some dance moves for the Monster Foot Bash.

Draw 3 things to make you shiver.

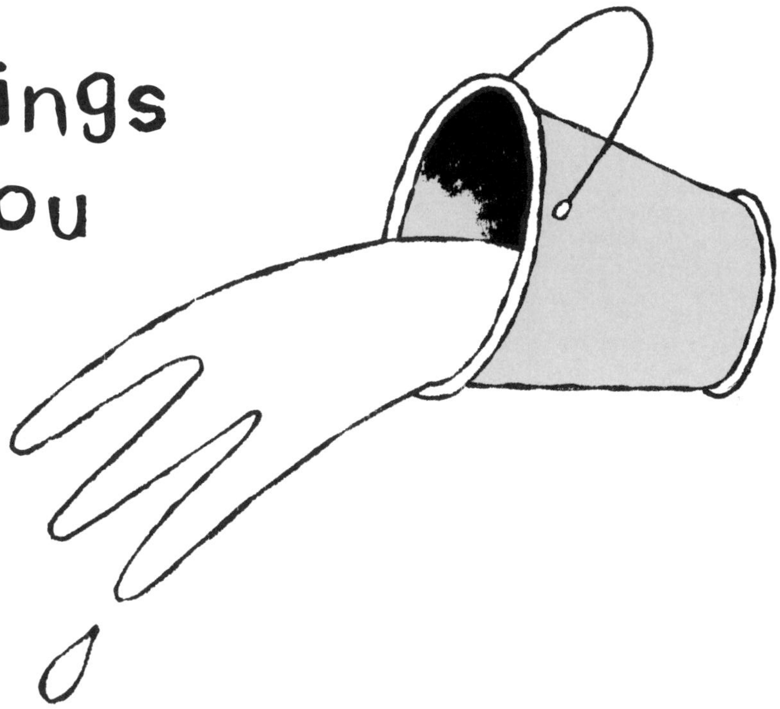

Draw an unwelcome mat.

Draw the front page news for the Daily Dreadful newspaper.

Draw some oozing boils on this monster's face.

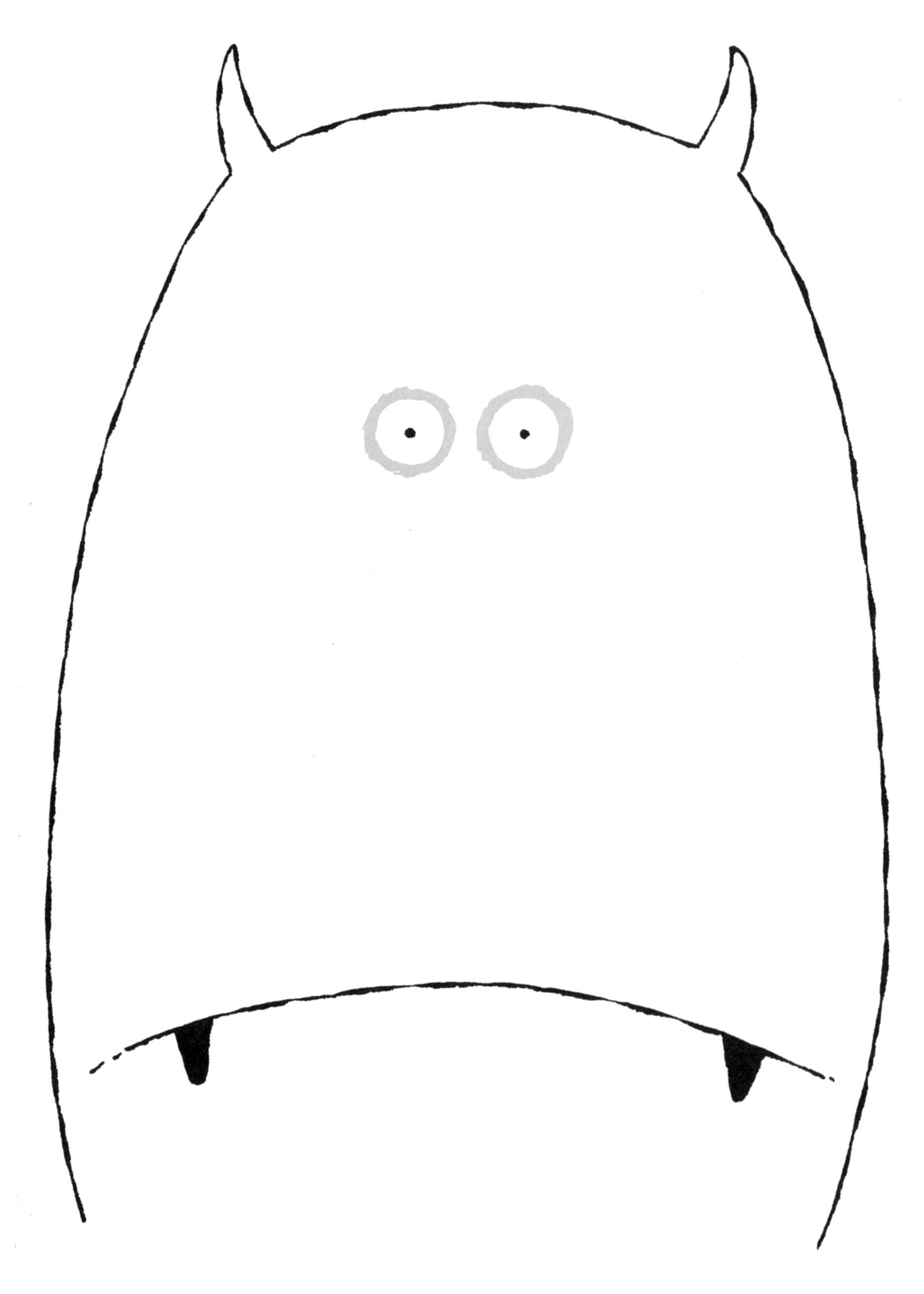

Draw some nasty spells on these shelves.

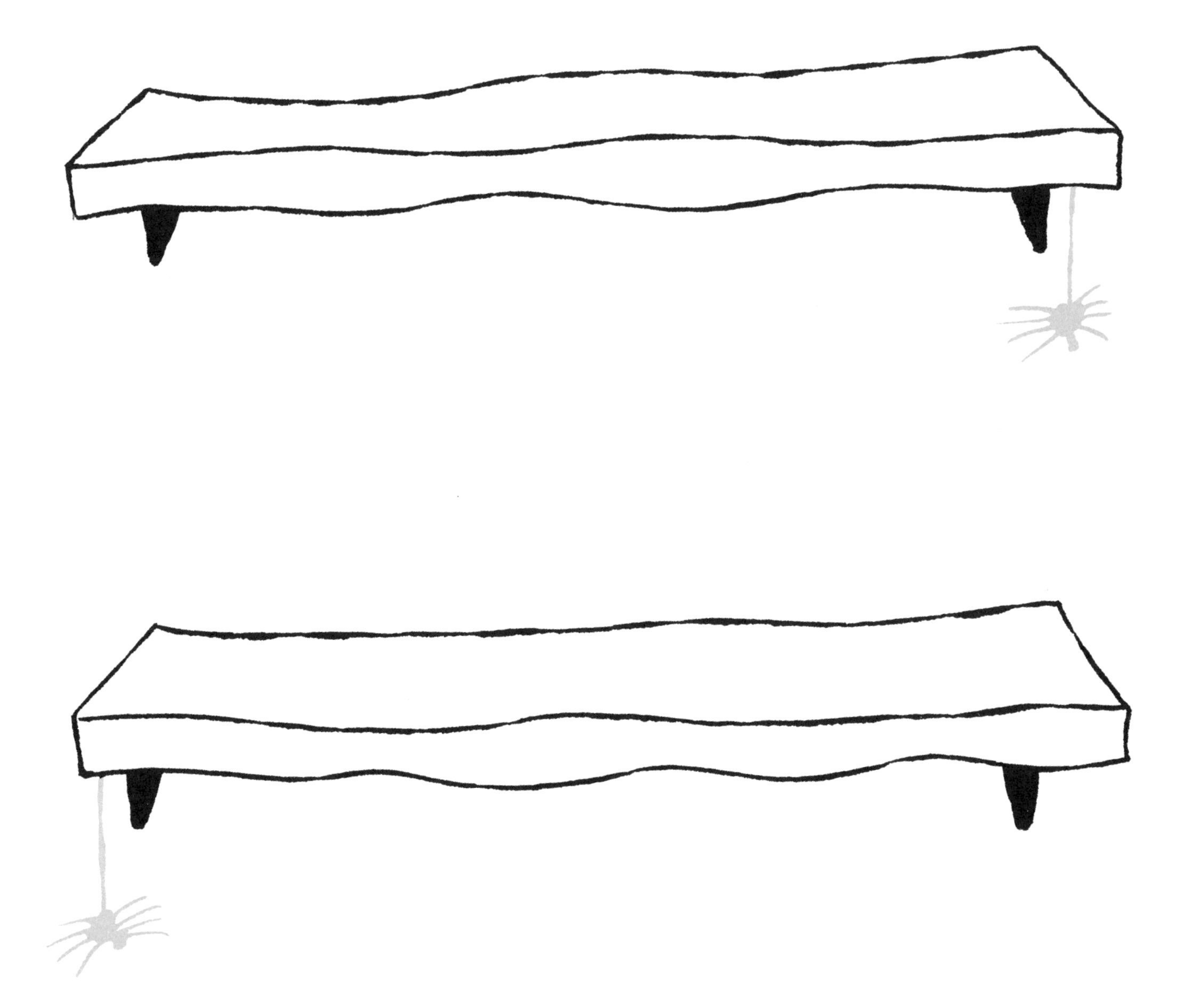

Draw the creatures that make these creepy shadows.

Draw tails for these creatures.

Draw a giant ship-munching sea worm.

Draw some
ingredients for
a cauldron party.

Draw a clammy handshake (or three).

Draw a night gurgler.

Gurgle!

Draw how you might cross these sinking sands.

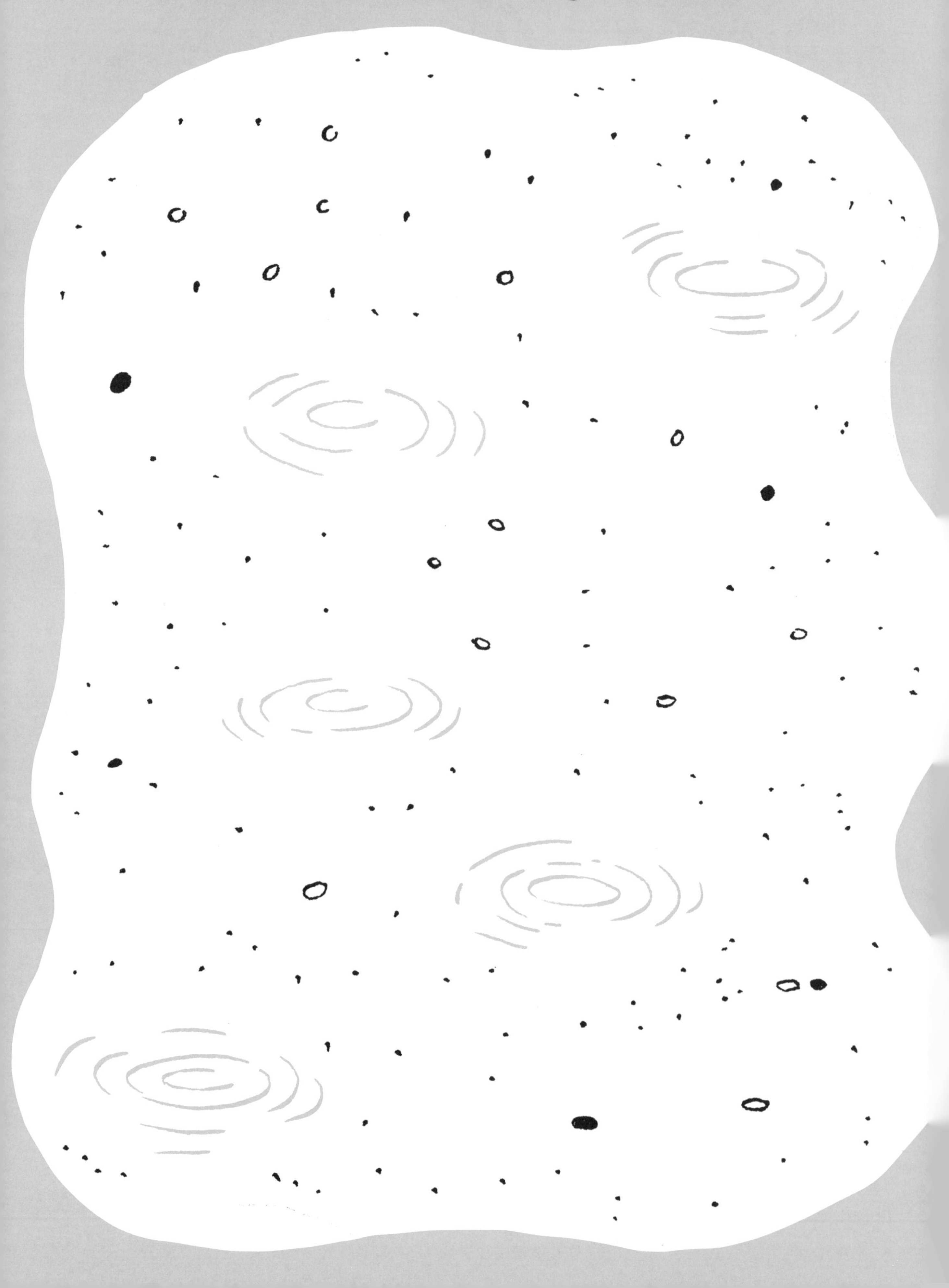

Draw
a baby
vampire
learning
to fly.

Draw the
winner of
this year's
stinky prize.

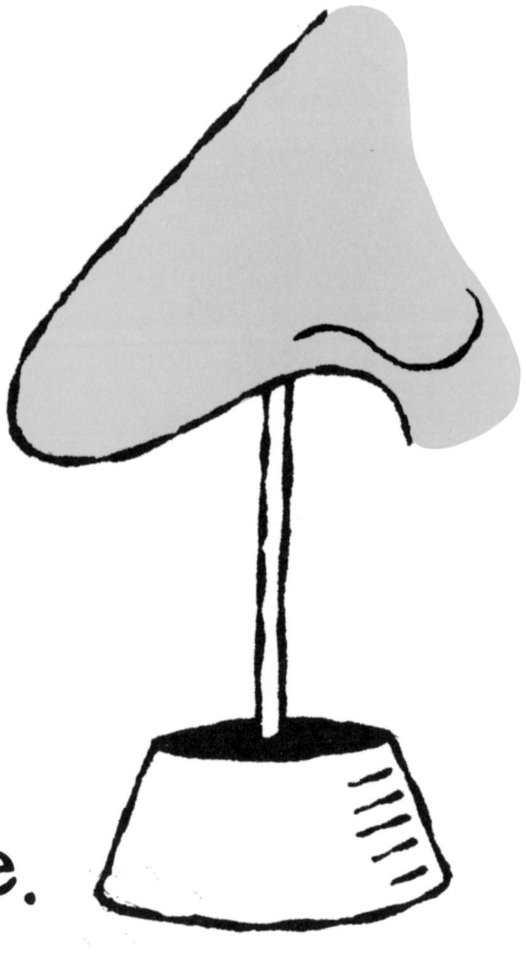

Draw how these bones might fit together.

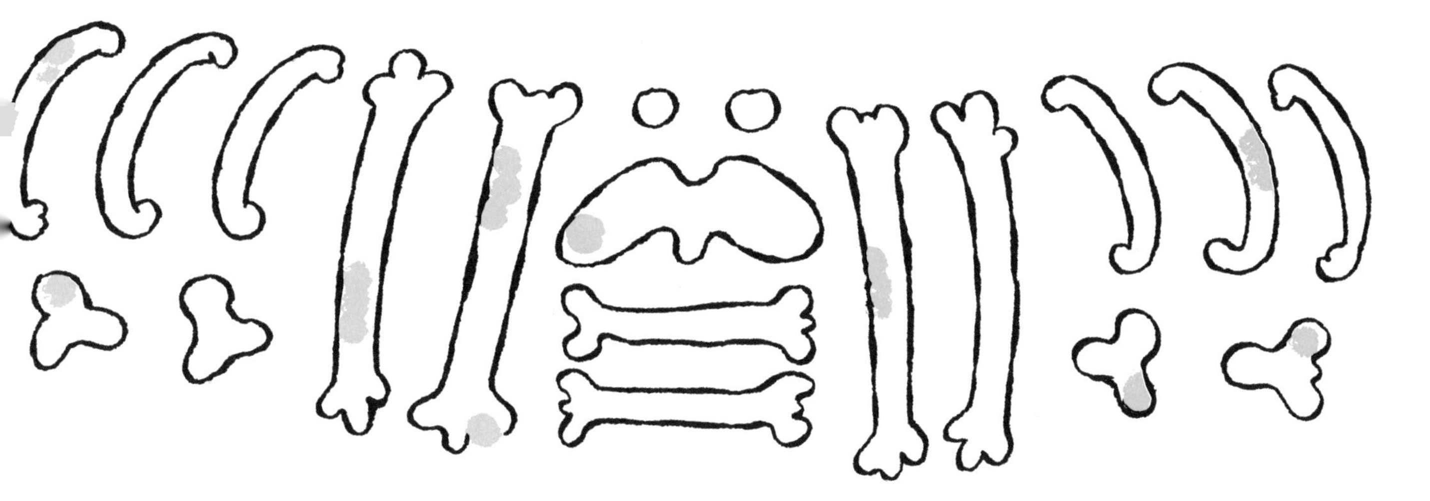

Draw Frankenstein's monster on a skateboard.

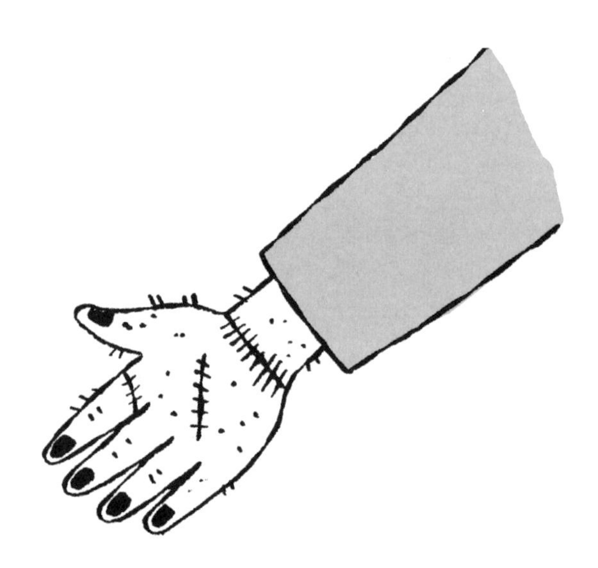

Draw something horrid under this bed.

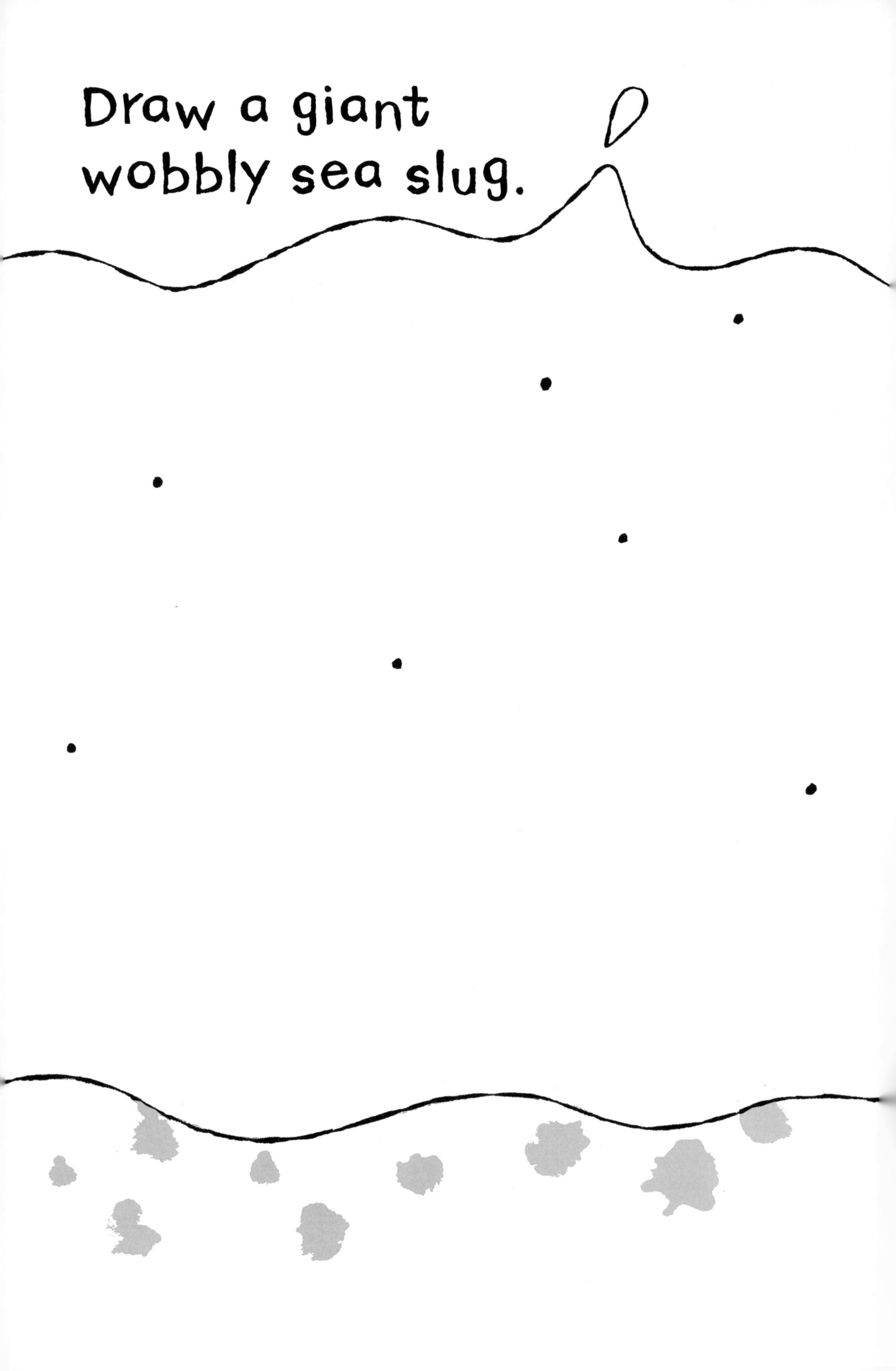
Draw a giant
wobbly sea slug.

Draw a toy for this baby gargoyle.

Draw an anti-vampire kit.

Draw a
ready
steady
slime
cake.

Draw a stench.

Draw a before and after poster for the monsters' dental clinic.

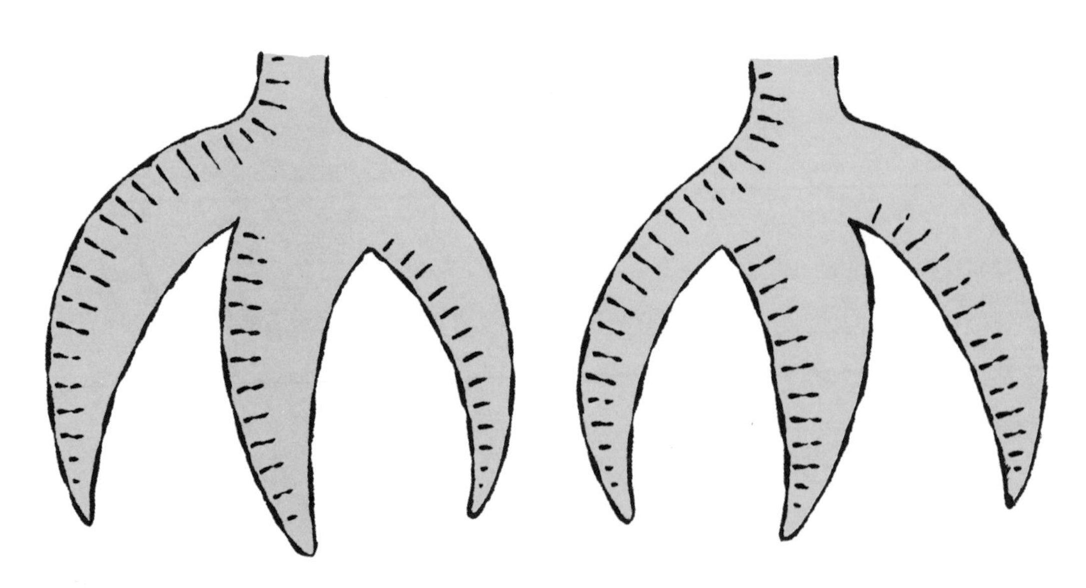

Draw the owner
of these claws.

Draw what's inside this little monster's party bag.

Draw some finger fungus.

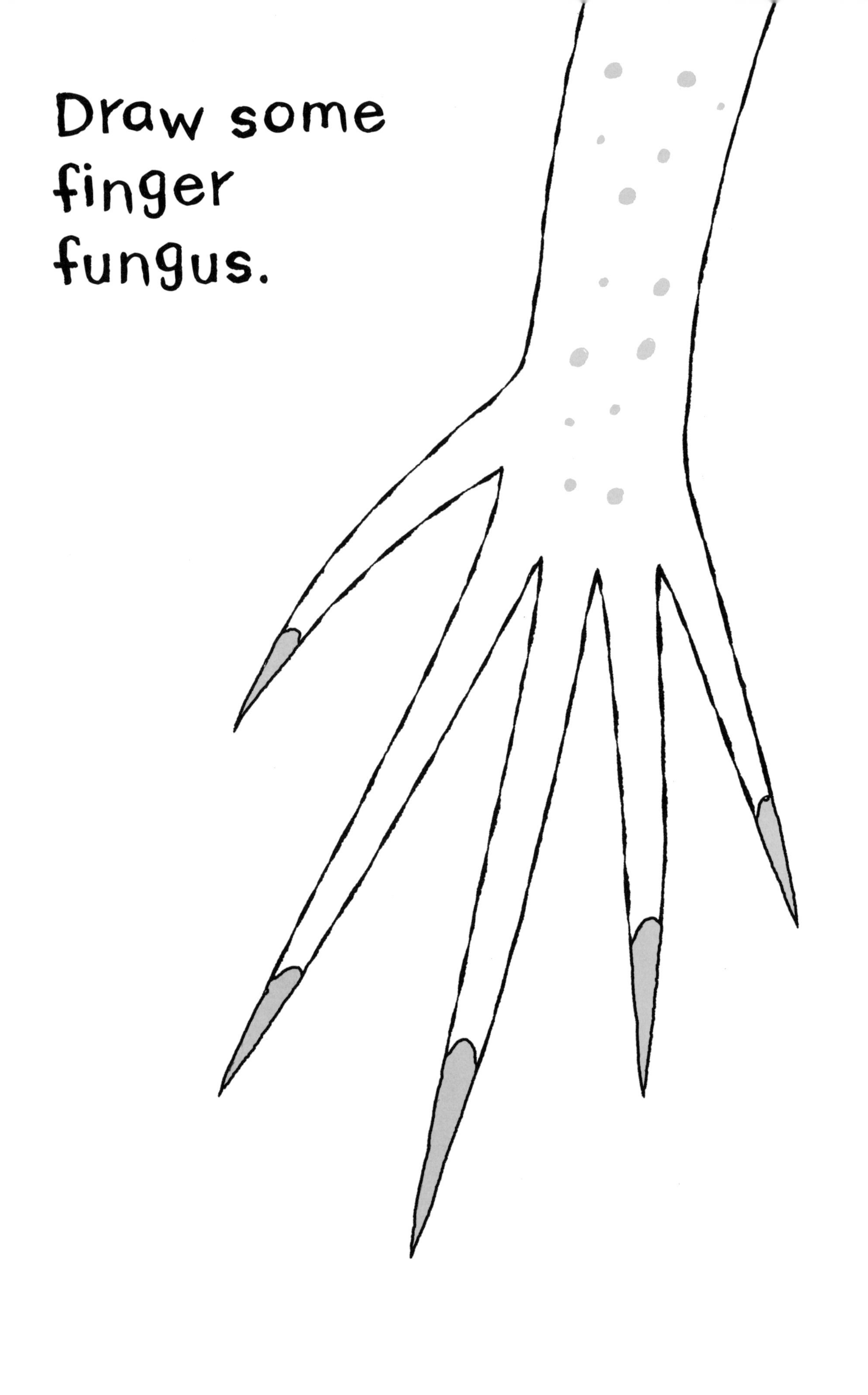

Draw who lives in this haunted tower.
Howl
Groan

Draw something disgusting in this bottle.

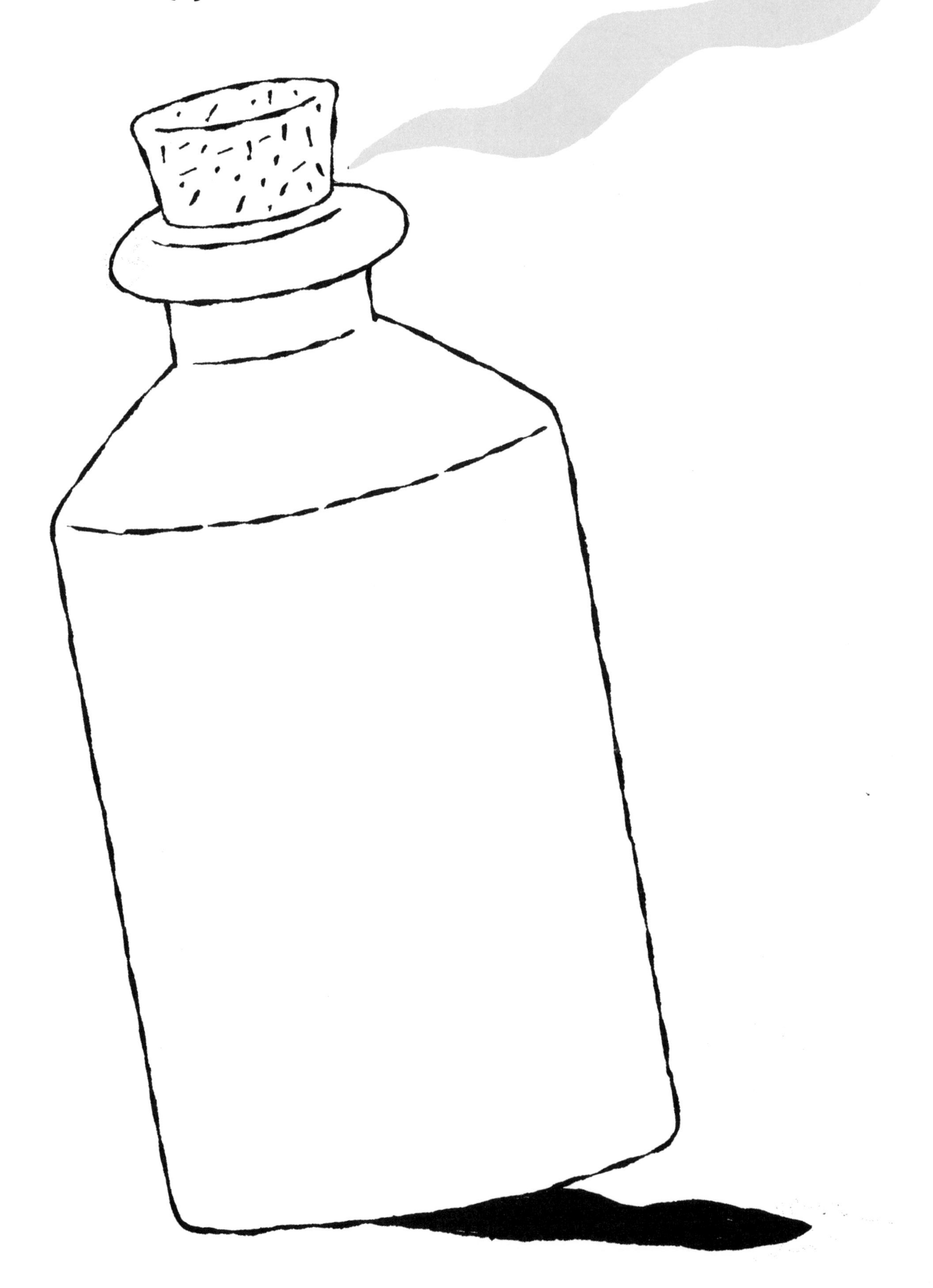

Draw a monster with a stomach ache.

Draw a housewarming gift for a witch.